# Pixel
## STICKER
## ART

# PIXEL ART

A pixel is the tiniest part of a digital image. The stickers in this book are your chance to be a pixel artist — to create cool images in your space. Make pixel figures to interact with your surroundings, decorate your stuff, or leave a sign or a visual joke for passers-by. Artists have been having fun with pixels for centuries — long before the word was invented.

Simple "points" of color make up the whole design.

The eye translates the dots into a range of shapes and colors.

## Pointillism

French artists Georges Seurat and Paul Signac developed a technique in 1886 that uses simple dots to make up complex images. The eye and mind mix the individual color spots into a fuller range, just as arrangements of pixels, in the viewer's eyes, become recognizable images.

Part of *La Parade de Cirque*, or *Circus Parade*, by Georges Seurat

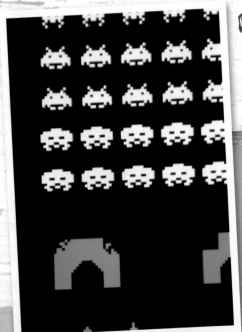

The alien graphic is recognized all over the world.

## Computer graphics

Aliens first appeared on screens in 1978 in an arcade game called Space Invaders. Though techniques have come a long way since then, the original pixelated characters are still hugely popular.

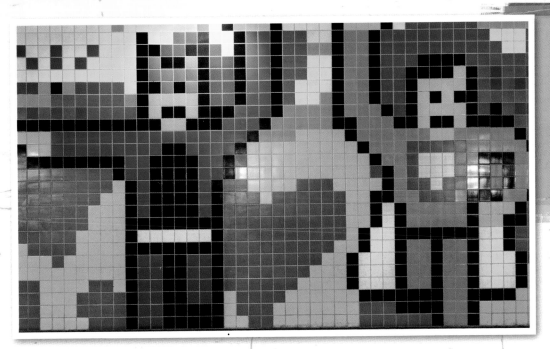

## Pixel mosaics

Colored tiles are the pixels in this mosaic mural that lines a bicycle tunnel in the Netherlands. The designers gave local people 16 different colors to work with, and asked them to submit designs pixel by pixel on a special website.

Participants follow directions by looking through slits in their cards.

## Card Stunts

The crowd at this American football game becomes the artist and "performs" the pixel art. Each person holds a colored card that forms part of a single image. Some card stunts use cards with a different color on each side — or flip books — so the big picture can be changed or even appear to "move."

## 3-D Pixel sculpture

Digital Orca, a killer whale sculpture by Canadian artist Douglas Coupland, makes a 3-D splash in Vancouver harbor. Made from metal cubes and lighting elements, this is pixel art you can enjoy from all angles.

Now it's your turn to be the artist!

3

# HOW TO DO IT

The easy-to-follow grids show you how to make any of the designs on the following pages. You'll find **16** pages of colored peelable stickers at the back of the book.

## 1 Choose a design

If you're new to sticker art, start with one of the simpler designs.

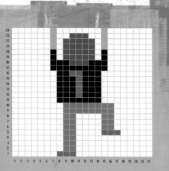

## 2 Find a suitable space

The stickers work best on a smooth flat surface — if it doesn't belong to you, it's best to ask permission before you start!

## 3 Make sure the design will fit

The design's height and width are shown above each grid. If you prefer to use metric measurements, flip to the back of the book where you'll find a conversion chart.

## 4 Peel off the stickers and stick them down, following the pattern laid out on the design grid. The stickers always go with the long sides top and bottom, the short sides on the right and left. Place them lightly at first, then it's easy to peel and adjust till you're happy with your design.

## Start sticking

• at the top if you want your image to hang

• at the bottom if you want it to stand.

Line up the stickers carefully, and place them edge to edge with no overlaps. It's a good idea to have a ruler or other straight edge handy to make sure your finished design stands, hangs, or flies straight.

**HINT**

# SCALING UP

The stickers in this book are the perfect size for pixel art designs — but you can think bigger, too. Follow the grid in exactly the same way, but make the "pixels" bigger by using sticky notes. These come in several sizes:

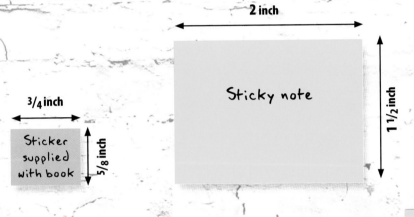

3/4 inch

Sticker supplied with book

5/8 inch

2 inch

Sticky note

1 1/2 inch

4 1/2 inch

Sticky note

3 inch

Using the 1 1/2-inch-high sticky notes would make the dino-monster (page 31) just under six feet tall — scary enough to make you run. If you used the 3-inch notes, he would be nearly twelve feet tall!

5

## FROWNY EMOTICON

TOTAL: **20 stickers**
SIZE: **6 3/4 x 6 1/4 inches**

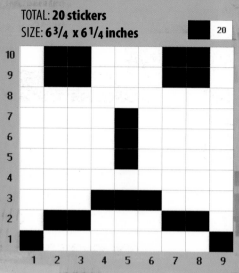

## WINKING EMOTICON

TOTAL: **18 stickers**
SIZE: **6 3/4 x 6 1/4 inches**

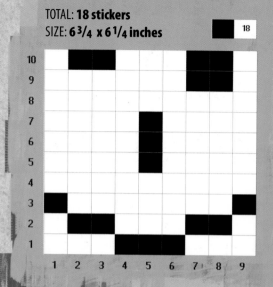

## SMILEY EMOTICON

TOTAL: **20 stickers**
SIZE: **6 3/4 x 6 1/4 inches**

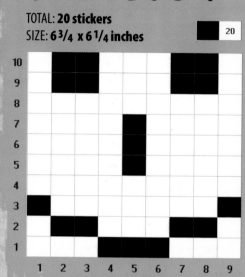

Leave a thank
you note — or say
"Hi!" — with
a smile.

Put on a happy face or give
the world a wink — depending
how you feel. Lunchbox, school
bag, card or note to friend: all
so much more fun with a face.

# NUMBERS

**TOTAL: 6 stickers**
**SIZE: 1 ½ x 3 ⅛ inches**

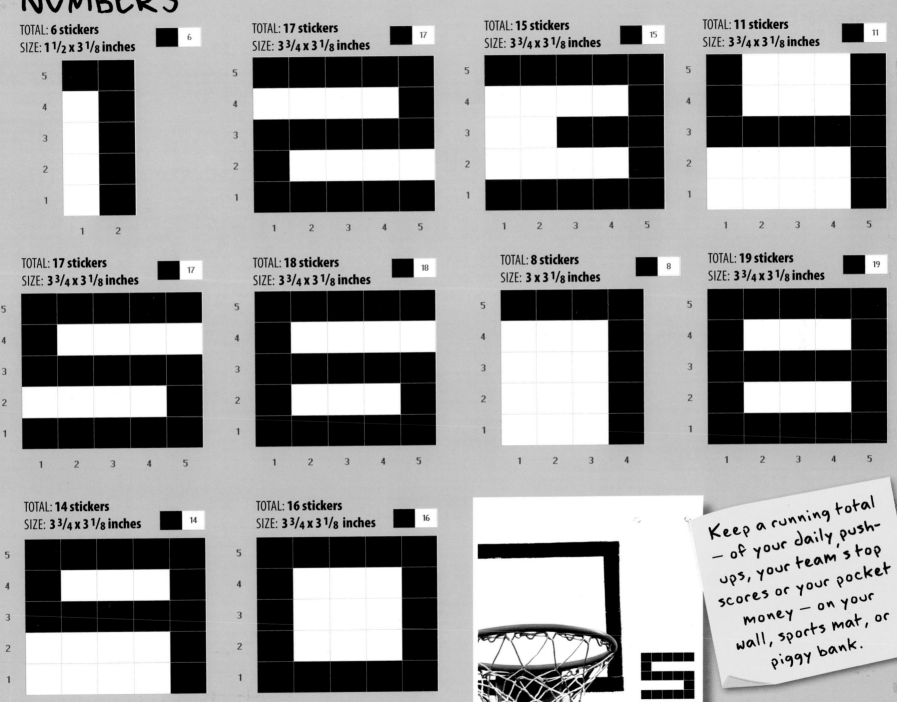

TOTAL: 17 stickers
SIZE: 3 ¾ x 3 ⅛ inches

TOTAL: 15 stickers
SIZE: 3 ¾ x 3 ⅛ inches

TOTAL: 11 stickers
SIZE: 3 ¾ x 3 ⅛ inches

TOTAL: 17 stickers
SIZE: 3 ¾ x 3 ⅛ inches

TOTAL: 18 stickers
SIZE: 3 ¾ x 3 ⅛ inches

TOTAL: 8 stickers
SIZE: 3 x 3 ⅛ inches

TOTAL: 19 stickers
SIZE: 3 ¾ x 3 ⅛ inches

TOTAL: 14 stickers
SIZE: 3 ¾ x 3 ⅛ inches

TOTAL: 16 stickers
SIZE: 3 ¾ x 3 ⅛ inches

Keep a running total — of your daily push-ups, your team's top scores or your pocket money — on your wall, sports mat, or piggy bank.

# ALPHABET

**TOTAL: 16 stickers**
SIZE: 3 3/4 x 3 1/8 inches — 16

**TOTAL: 17 stickers**
SIZE: 3 3/4 x 3 1/8 inches — 17

**TOTAL: 13 stickers**
SIZE: 3 3/4 x 3 1/8 inches — 13

**TOTAL: 14 stickers**
SIZE: 3 3/4 x 3 1/8 inches — 14

**TOTAL: 16 stickers**
SIZE: 3 3/4 x 3 1/8 inches — 16

**TOTAL: 12 stickers**
SIZE: 3 3/4 x 3 1/8 inches — 12

**TOTAL: 17 stickers**
SIZE: 3 3/4 x 3 1/8 inches — 17

**TOTAL: 13 stickers**
SIZE: 3 3/4 x 3 1/8 inches — 13

**TOTAL: 13 stickers**
SIZE: 3 3/4 x 3 1/8 inches — 13

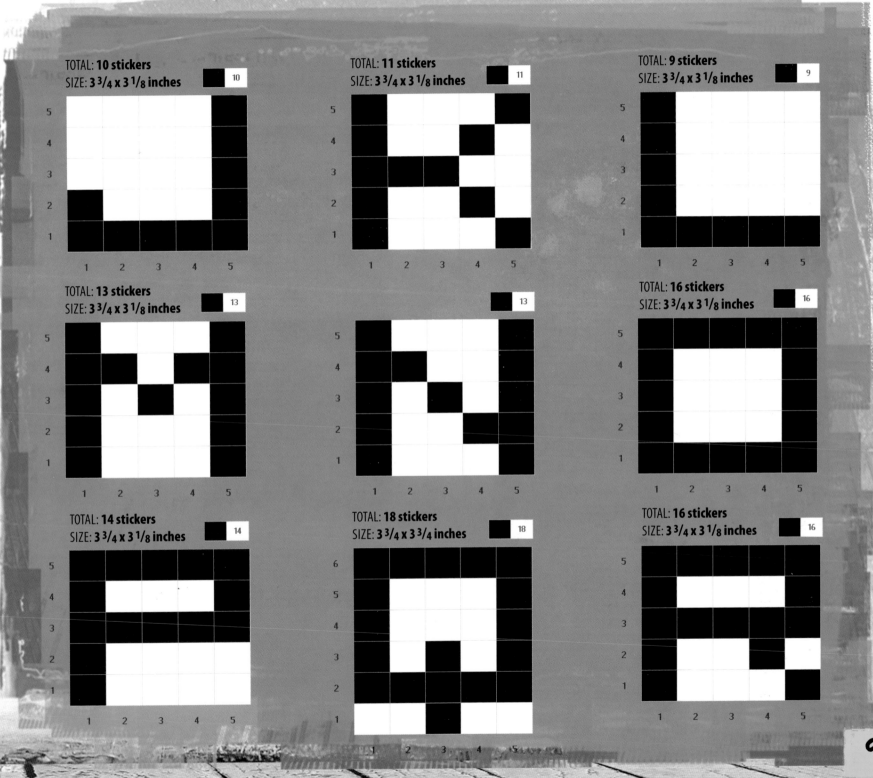

# ALPHABET

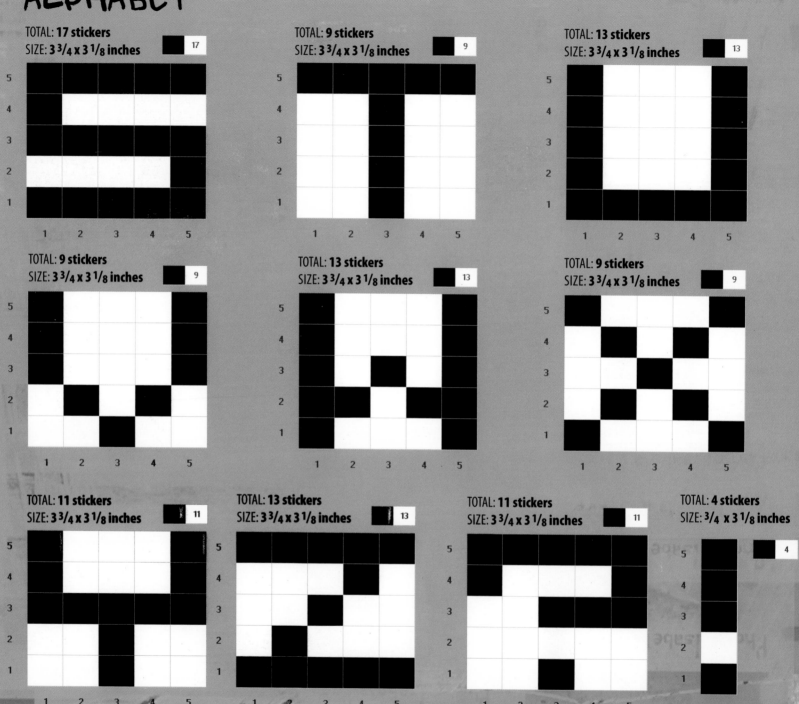

TOTAL: **17 stickers**
SIZE: 3 ¾ x 3 ⅛ inches  17

TOTAL: **9 stickers**
SIZE: 3 ¾ x 3 ⅛ inches  9

TOTAL: **13 stickers**
SIZE: 3 ¾ x 3 ⅛ inches  13

TOTAL: **9 stickers**
SIZE: 3 ¾ x 3 ⅛ inches  9

TOTAL: **13 stickers**
SIZE: 3 ¾ x 3 ⅛ inches  13

TOTAL: **9 stickers**
SIZE: 3 ¾ x 3 ⅛ inches  9

TOTAL: **11 stickers**
SIZE: 3 ¾ x 3 ⅛ inches  11

TOTAL: **13 stickers**
SIZE: 3 ¾ x 3 ⅛ inches  13

TOTAL: **11 stickers**
SIZE: 3 ¾ x 3 ⅛ inches  11

TOTAL: **4 stickers**
SIZE: ¾ x 3 ⅛ inches  4

BEWARE OF THE DOG

COME ON IN!

ENTER AT OWN RISK

Ask 'em in or keep 'em out: change your pixel greeting to match your mood.

# GHOST

TOTAL: **36 stickers**
SIZE: **6 3/4 x 5 inches**

| | 34 |
|---|---|
| | 2 |

Stick this spook behind the cellar door or in a dark corner — where better for a ghost to hide?

Trick or treat! Signal you're in a Halloween mood with a pumpkin on the front door.

# PUMPKIN

| | 1 |
|---|---|
| | 31 |
| | 7 |

TOTAL: **39 stickers**
SIZE: **5 1/4 x 4 3/8 inches**

# SPIDER

TOTAL: **51 stickers**
SIZE: **6 ¾ x 13 ⅛ inches**

| | |
| --- | --- |
| 14 | 13 |
| 20 | 2 |

# SKULL

TOTAL: **26 stickers**
SIZE: **5 ¼ x 4 ⅜ inches**

| | |
| --- | --- |
| 26 | |

Make your little brother jump or sister squeal: hang a beady-eyed spider over the bed or on the bathroom window.

Nothing spells KEEP OUT like a spooky skull: station this grisly guard on your private drawer or diary.

13

Lock up your secrets! Deter snoopers by keeping your stuff under lock and key.

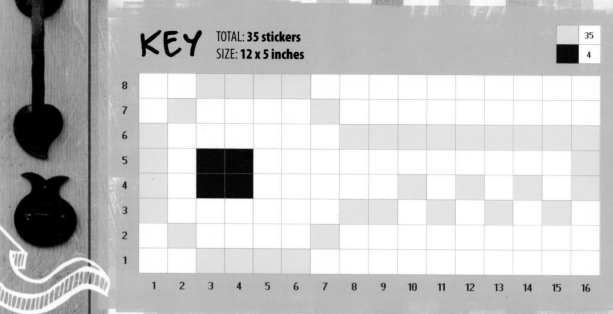

## KEY

**TOTAL: 35 stickers**
**SIZE: 12 x 5 inches**

| | 35 |
|---|---|
| | 4 |

## PADLOCK

**TOTAL: 45 stickers**
**SIZE: 4 1/4 x 6 1/4 inches**

| | 36 |
|---|---|
| | 9 |

Long live Space Invaders! But line up an anti-invader gun or two as well, just in case they bring reinforcements....

# ANTI-INVADER GUN

**TOTAL: 34 stickers**
**SIZE: 6 3/4 x 6 1/4 inches**

34

# RED INVADER

**TOTAL: 36 stickers**
**SIZE: 6 x 5 inches**

36

# GREEN INVADER

**TOTAL: 33 stickers**
**SIZE: 5 1/4 x 5 inches**

33

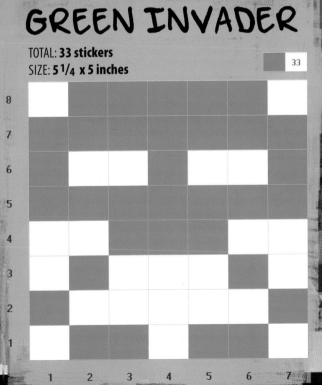

15

# EYE

**TOTAL: 27 stickers**
**SIZE: 7 1/2 x 4 3/8 inches**

| | 18 |
| --- | --- |
| | 9 |

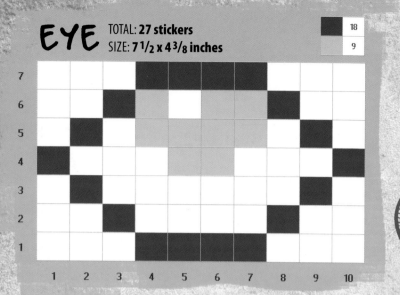

Unsettle your visitors by putting the all-seeing eye where they'd least like to be observed!

Move the pupil to direct the gaze where you want it. Why not add an eye, or two, to a poster or photograph?

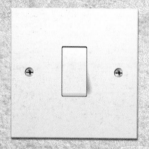

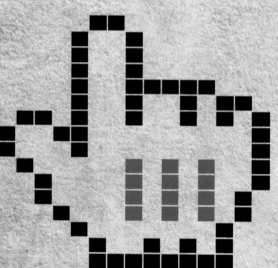

Something you'd like to point out? Use a pointy finger to make sure everyone knows just where to look.

# POINTY FINGER

**TOTAL: 67 stickers**
**SIZE: 11 1/4 x 10 inches**

| | 55 |
| --- | --- |
| | 12 |

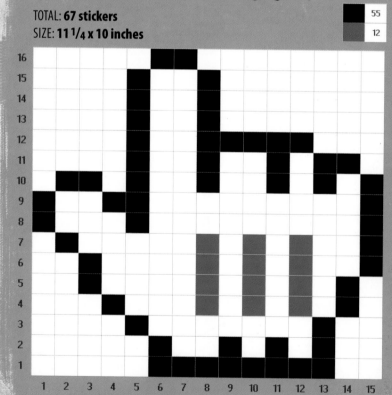

The classic icon that always brings a smile to a skateboard, chair back, locker, window, or . . . .

# SPRAY CAN

TOTAL: **60 stickers**
SIZE: **7 1/2 x 9 3/8 inches**

| | | | |
|---|---|---|---|
| | 37 | | 10 |
| | 10 | | 3 |

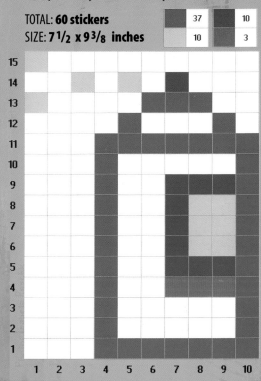

# SMILEY FACE

TOTAL: **60 stickers**
SIZE: **10 1/2 x 9 3/8 inches**

| | 60 |
|---|---|

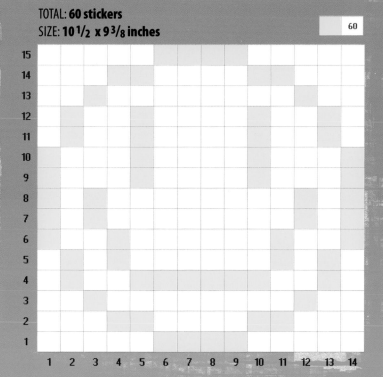

Be an urban artist without breaking the law! Put peelable graffiti where it can't be missed.

# GREEN ALIEN

**TOTAL:** 42 stickers
**SIZE:** 6 3/4 x 5 inches

| | | | |
|---|---|---|---|
| | 36 | | 2 |
| | 2 | | 2 |

# EXTRATERRESTRIAL

**TOTAL:** 66 stickers
**SIZE:** 6 3/4 x 10 inches

| | | | |
|---|---|---|---|
| | 41 | | 2 |
| | 22 | | 1 |

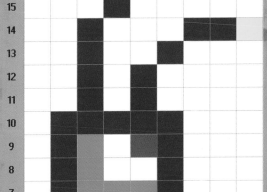

Bring a little
extraterrestrial cool
to your schoolbooks
— see if it helps with
the homework!

# MAIL SYMBOL

TOTAL: **40 stickers**
SIZE: **7 1/2 x 5 inches**

| | 40 |
|---|---|

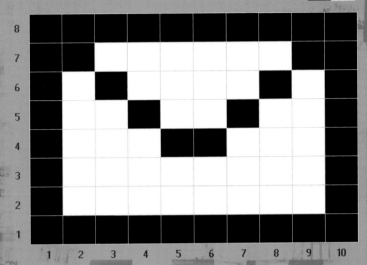

Style your own stationery — no stamp needed.

Leave a cool musical note on your instrument, music case, or notebook.

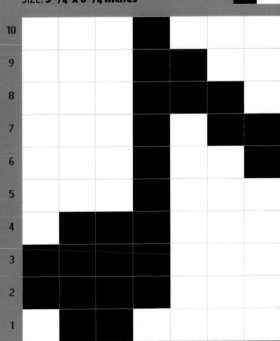

# MUSIC NOTE

TOTAL: **25 stickers**
SIZE: **5 1/4 x 6 1/4 inches**

| | 25 |
|---|---|

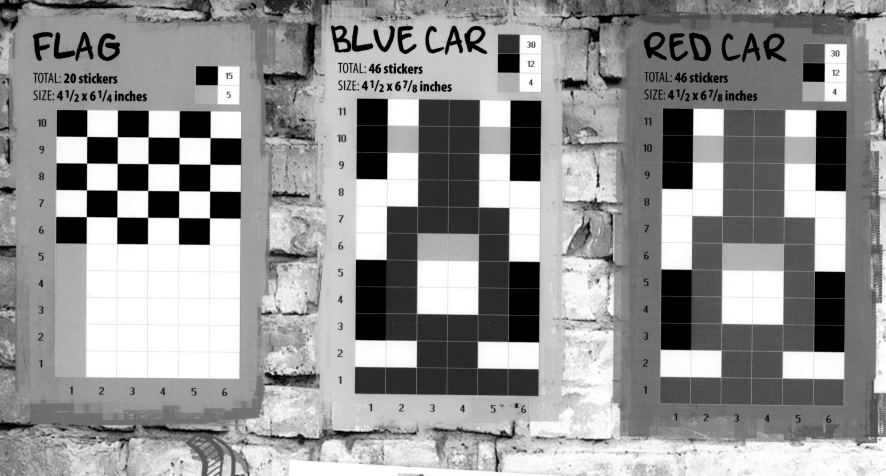

# FLAG

**TOTAL: 20 stickers**
**SIZE: 4 1/2 x 6 1/4 inches**

| | 15 |
| | 5 |

# BLUE CAR

**TOTAL: 46 stickers**
**SIZE: 4 1/2 x 6 7/8 inches**

| | 30 |
| | 12 |
| | 4 |

# RED CAR

**TOTAL: 46 stickers**
**SIZE: 4 1/2 x 6 7/8 inches**

| | 30 |
| | 12 |
| | 4 |

These cars will race on floors or walls — their high-performance tires even hold the road when they're upside-down on the ceiling!

## SPEECH BUBBLE

TOTAL: **30 stickers**
SIZE: 8 1/4 x 6 1/4 inches

# BEE

**TOTAL: 34 stickers**
**SIZE: 6 x 6 7/8 inches**

| | |
|---|---|
| 14 | 6 |
| 12 | 2 |

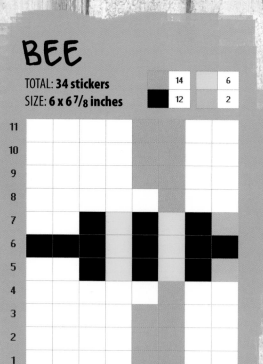

Make summer come early... plant flowers along your shelves and have bees and butterflies at the window.

# BUTTERFLY

**TOTAL: 112 stickers**
**SIZE: 10 1/2 x 8 1/8 inches**

| | |
|---|---|
| 54 |
| 48 |
| 10 |

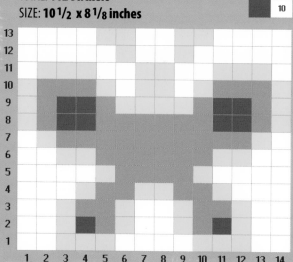

# FLOWER

**TOTAL: 16 stickers**
**SIZE: 2 1/4 x 5 inches**

| | |
|---|---|
| 7 |
| 4 |
| 4 |
| 1 |

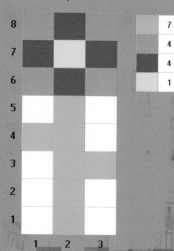

# WHALE

**TOTAL: 114 stickers**
**SIZE: 13 ½ x 11 ¼ inches**

| | 78 |
| | 36 |

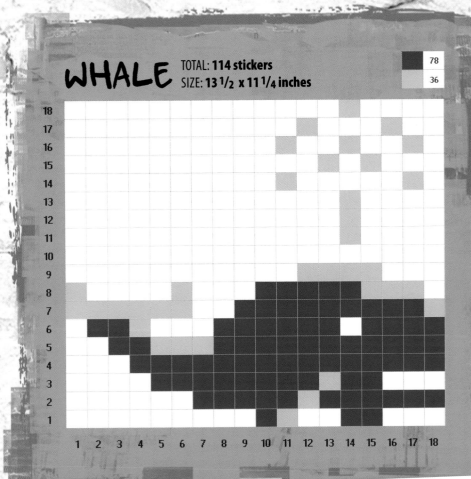

Forecast your own good weather! A little sunshine on the window improves even the darkest day.

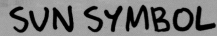

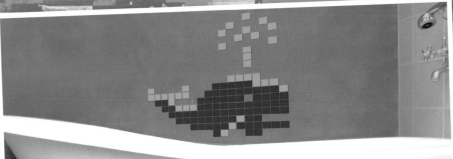

Have a whale leap out of the bath or splash above the sink. Surprise your goldfish with a new friend!

# SUN SYMBOL

**TOTAL: 55 stickers**
**SIZE: 9 ¾ x 9 ⅜ inches**

| | 55 |

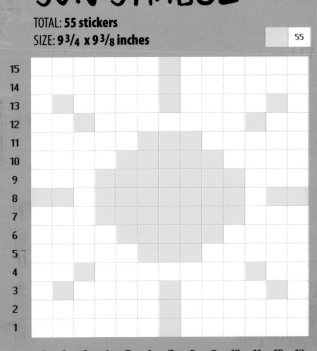

## LEANING MAN

**TOTAL: 51 stickers**
**SIZE: 7 1/2 x 8 3/4 inches**

| | 18 | | 11 |
|---|---|---|---|
| | 16 | | 6 |

He never tires! Leaning man will "hold" your books in place or your doorframe upright ... and won't give up until you peel him off.

## VOLUME SYMBOL

**TOTAL: 23 stickers**
**SIZE: 6 3/4 x 5 5/8 inches**

| | 18 |
|---|---|
| | 5 |

Add a LOUD symbol to speakers to ramp up the volume — without disturbing the neighbors!

26

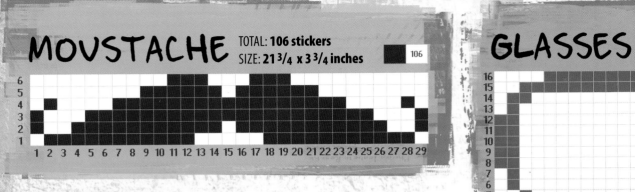

# MOUSTACHE

**TOTAL:** 106 stickers
**SIZE:** 21 ³/₄ x 3 ³/₄ inches

106

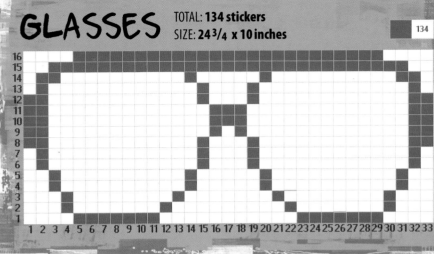

# GLASSES

**TOTAL:** 134 stickers
**SIZE:** 24 ³/₄ x 10 inches

134

Position the moustache on the bathroom mirror and give yourself a whole new look. Add glasses to complete the effect.

If face furniture isn't your style, accessorize a poster or photograph for an instant pixel disguise.

27

# HEART

**TOTAL:** 26 stickers
**SIZE:** 5 1/4 x 3 3/4 inches

| | 26 |
|---|---|

Leave a heartwarming sign for someone to find in a drawer or a book, on a note, or a mug.

# CLIMBING MAN

**TOTAL:** 125 stickers
**SIZE:** 8 1/4 x 15 inches

| | 43 | | 28 | | 8 |
|---|---|---|---|---|---|
| | 32 | | 14 | | |

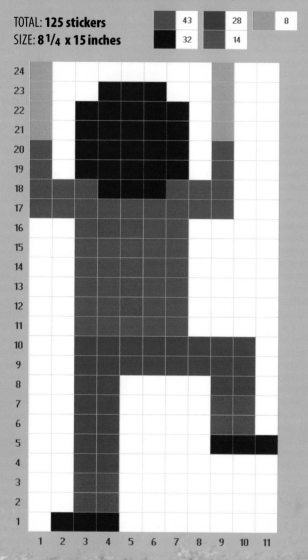

Is he trying to climb in or climb out?

Hang the climbing man by his fingertips from the ceiling or stand him on the ground — you decide whether he's going up or down.

# ROBOT

**TOTAL:** 181 stickers
**SIZE:** 12 3/4 x 15 inches

| | |
|---|---|
| ■ 78 | ■ 26 | □ 2 |
| ■ 63 | ■ 12 | |

Position the fire-breathing dino-monster so he scorches the view from your window. Singe a neighboring building or treetop!

This is a great design to scale up. Use larger sticky notes instead of pixel stickers to make him tower over your tallest friends.

Number One robot awaits your instruction. Make him stand by your bed or above your desk, or let him guard your games.

You could add another robot, vary the colors and change the red number on his chest (see numbers, page 7) to have ranks of robots at your service!

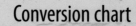

## Conversion chart

| inches | millimeters |
|--------|-------------|
| 1/8 | 3 |
| 1/4 | 6 |
| 3/8 | 10 |
| 1/2 | 13 |
| 5/8 | 16 |
| 3/4 | 19 |
| 7/8 | 22 |

| inches | centimeters |
|--------|-------------|
| 1 | 2.5 |
| 2 | 5 |
| 3 | 7.6 |
| 4 | 10.1 |
| 5 | 12.7 |
| 6 | 15.2 |
| 7 | 17.7 |
| 8 | 20.3 |
| 9 | 22.8 |
| 10 | 25.4 |

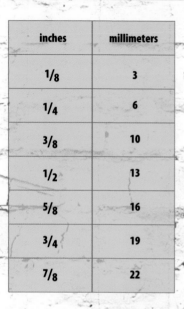

This edition published by Scholastic Inc.,
557 Broadway, New York, NY 10012,
by arrangement with Quarto Publishing

Scholastic and associated logos
are trademarks and/or registered
trademarks of Scholastic Inc.

Distributed by Scholastic Canada Ltd.,
Markham, Ontario

ISBN: 978-0-545-47434-4

10 9 8 7 6 5 4 3 2 1

**Picture Credits**
Key: t = top, b = bottom, r = right, l = left, c = center

Page 2 br, Page 3 bc: Kivett Productions www.cardstunts.com
Page 2 bl, tr; Page 3 tl, cr: Alamy
All other images: Shutterstock

**Author** Matthew Kelly,
**Design** Laura Hambleton, Andrew Crowson
**Senior Editor** Diane Pengelly
**Art Director** Jonathan Gilbert
**Publisher** Sue Grabham

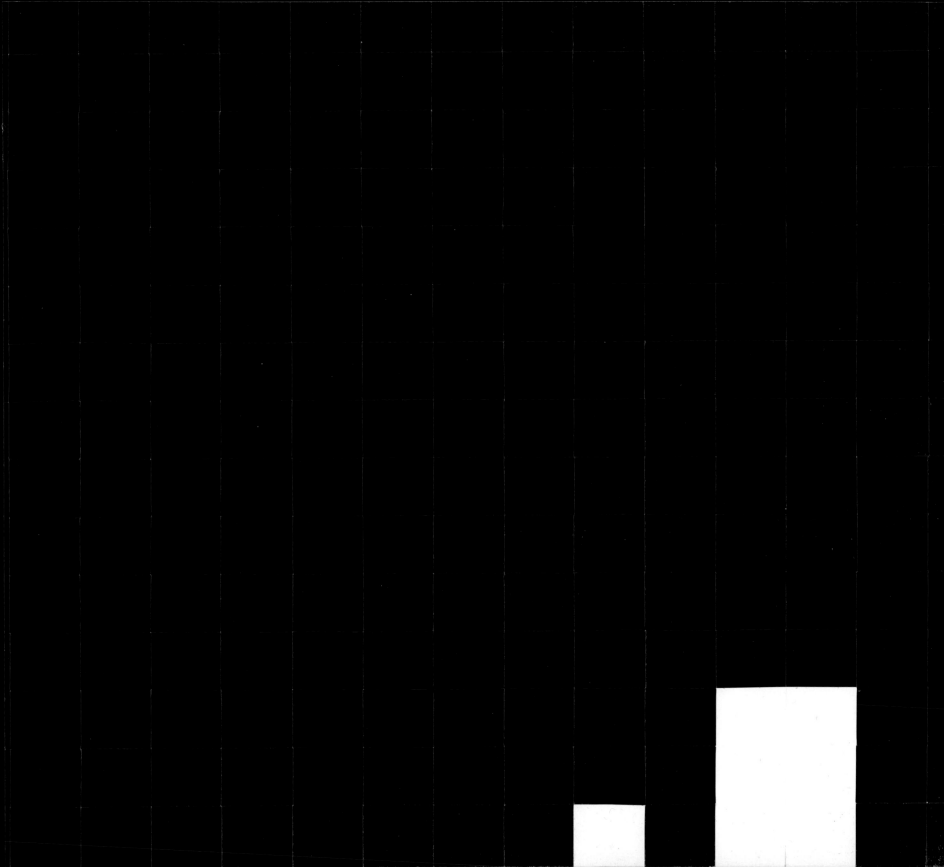

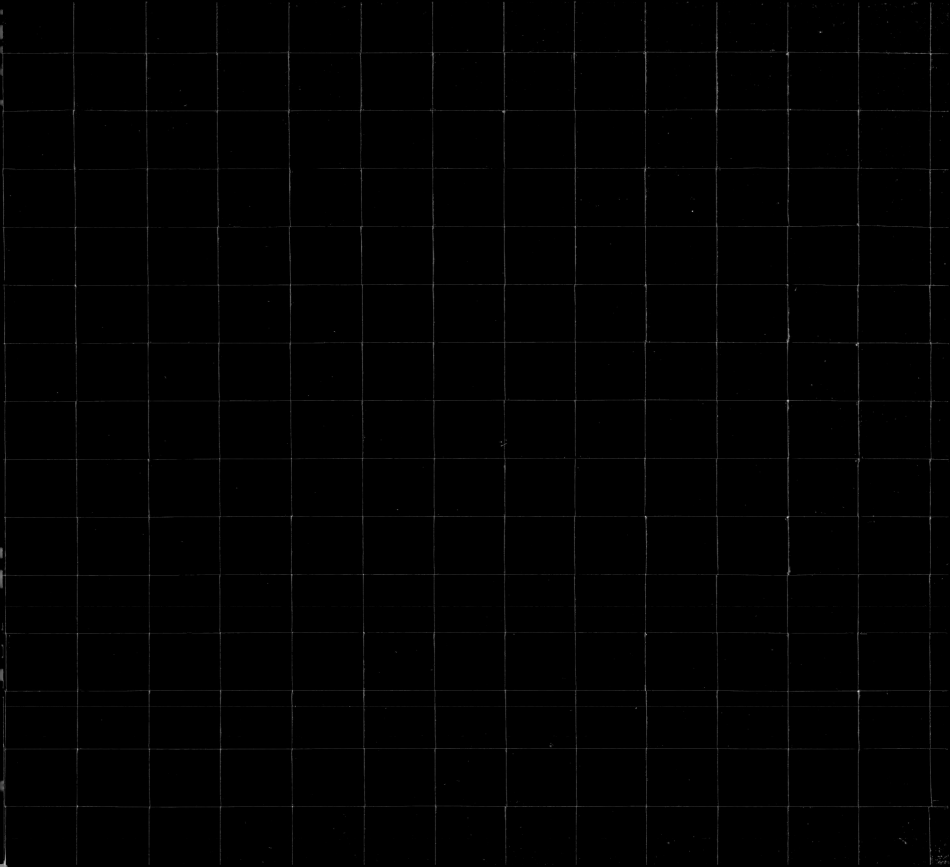